MOUTHFOOL

A GOURMET COLLECTION OF CULINARY CARTOONS

apicella

A MARK BRYANT BOOK

GRUB STREET • LONDON

Published by Grub Street, The Basement,
10 Chivalry Road, London SW11 1HT

Copyright © 1993 Grub Street and Mark Bryant
Copyright cartoons © 1993 Enzo Apicella

The moral right of the author has been asserted

British Library Cataloguing in Publication Data
Apicella, Enzo
Mouthfool
I. Title
741.5

ISBN 0-948817-87-9

*Back cover photograph of Apicella and friend
by Stefano Archetti.*

ACKNOWLEDGEMENTS

Some of the cartoons in the book originally appeared
in the *Observer*, *Guardian*, *Private Eye* and *Harpers &
Queen* and are reproduced with the kind permission of
the proprietors of those magazines. I would also like
to thank George Melly for his magnificent foreword,
Mark Bryant for helping turn the idea into a book and
all at Grub Street Publishing for producing such a
handsome volume, and, of course, all the chefs -
without whom none of it would have been possible.

**Enzo Apicella
London, 1993**

A Paolo e Antonio

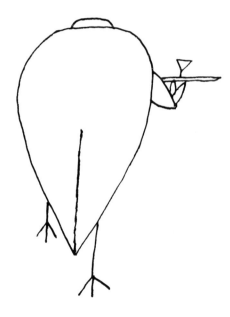

FOREWORD

Thinking of Apicella, I see him clearly lounging in an easy chair in the lobby of his elegant restaurant near South Kensington Underground station at the posh end of the Fulham Road - only of course it wasn't him but an alarmingly life-like dummy. A typical, slightly unnerving joke!

He has always presented an enigma. On the surface there is that irresistible Italian charm, that apparently effortless elegance; both characteristics much prized by the restrained, rather gauche British, and indeed qualities which have loosened us up a lot over the past thirty years or so. There are hidden depths, however.

It was the Italians in general and Apicella in particular who first understood that the pop revolution demanded more of eating out than a rather gloomy ritual conducted in a church-like ambience. They brought in cool white spaces, tiled floors, modern furniture. The cosy old Italian restaurants, still extant, of course, were challenged by these dashing parvenues and their excessively handsome waiters brandishing their enormous phallic pepper mills. For the popocracy the relaxed yet subtly exclusive atmosphere was ideal.

The décor usually went for modern works of art: framed exhibition posters, prints and photographs; but Apicella went further. To my knowledge he was the first restaurateur in this country to exhibit unselfconsciously contemporary work; an old tradition, of course, in France. On the roof of his Fulham Road flagship, for instance, directly above his reclining *doppelgänger*, was a large uncompromising sculpture by Paolozzi causing, no doubt, much adverse comment from the elderly ladies of the neighbourhood. Here, as elsewhere, Apicella went a little further than any of his colleagues or contemporaries. There was always, and it was part of his attraction, the hint of an edge.

And nowhere is this more clearly exposed than in his cartoons, for Enzo is also a cartoonist. On second thought that 'also' is wrongly judged. It suggests a small extra accomplishment, the scraping of Ingre's violin. In reality his cartoons are a major talent displaying an economy of line and the exploitation of space which put him, in my view, into the same class as our mutual friend, the late Mark Boxer. The fact Apicella is also a restaurateur is interesting but irrelevant.

In the instance of this book, however, there is a bearing, not in artistry but in subject matter. *MOUTHFOOL: A Gourmet Collection of Culinary Cartoons* offers an insider's guide to the ever-more hysterical , hype-ridden, and over-the-top world of contemporary eating, and in particular the elevation of the chef into an approximation of operatic diva, rock star and licensed psychopath. Apicella views it all with magisterial detachment but, while much of his subject matter is of a more general if still gastronomic nature, his image of a pack of ravening beasts, naked except for chef's hats and bearing down on a panicking restaurant peopled by tiny creatures should be hung over every customer-ejecting ego-maniac's kitchen range.

This is a wonderfully funny book, just the right length to keep us calm and amused during one of those suspiciously long waits between courses.

George Melly

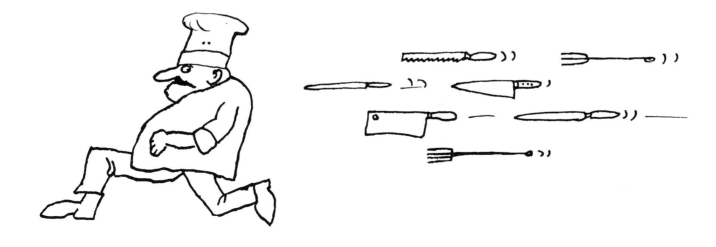

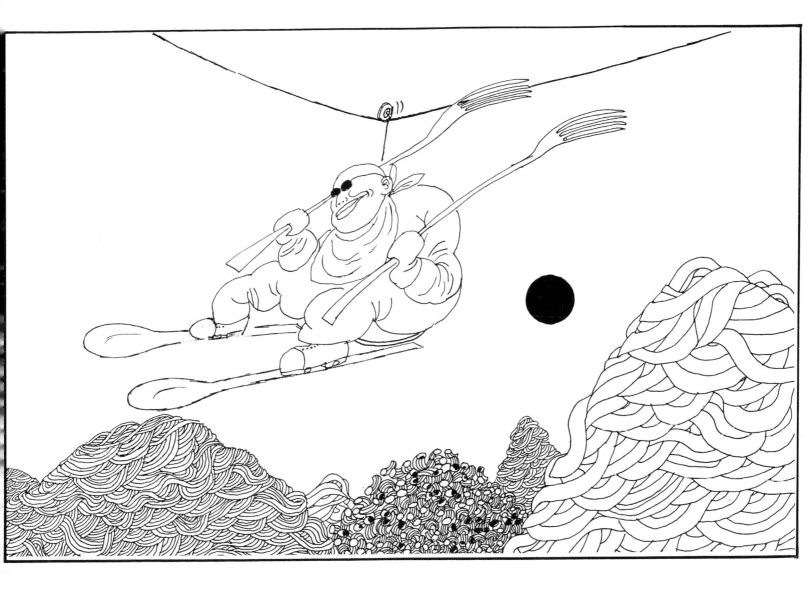

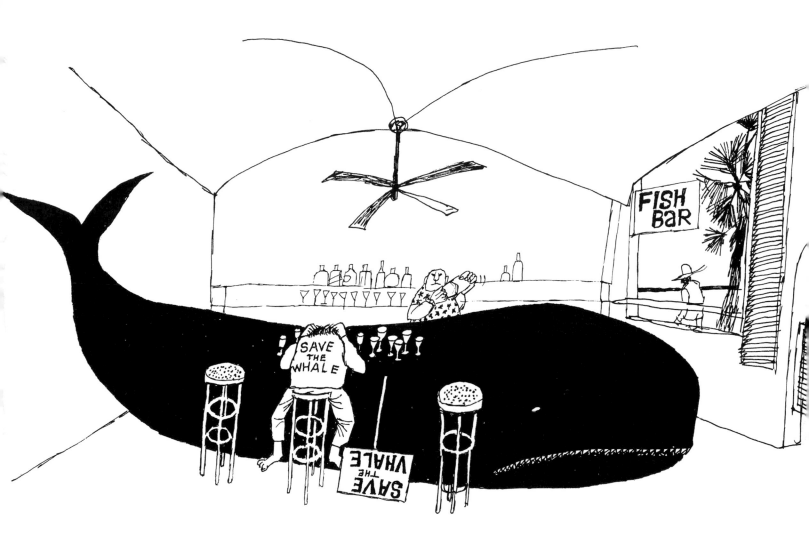

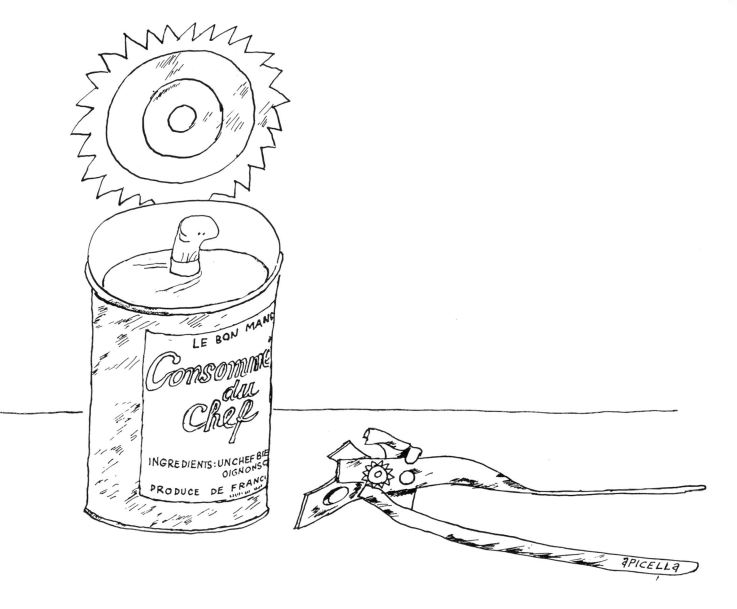

Apicella '86

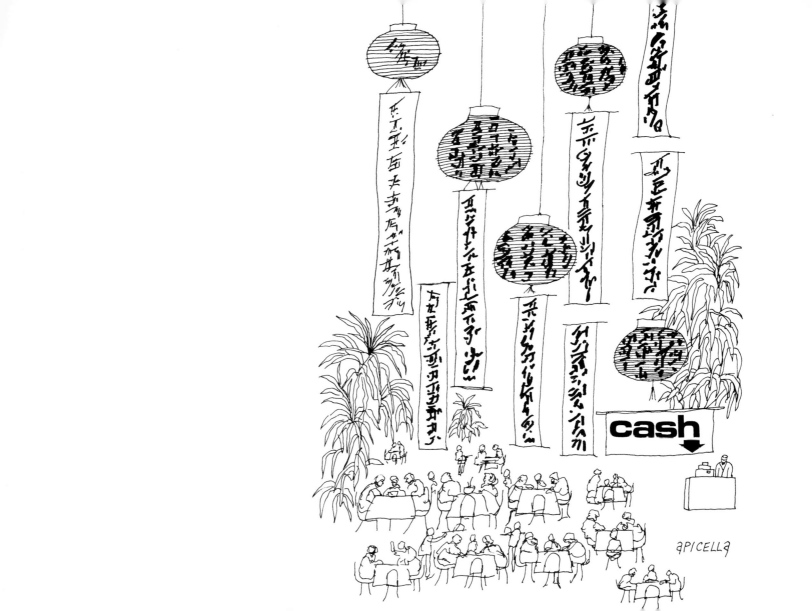

cash

apicella

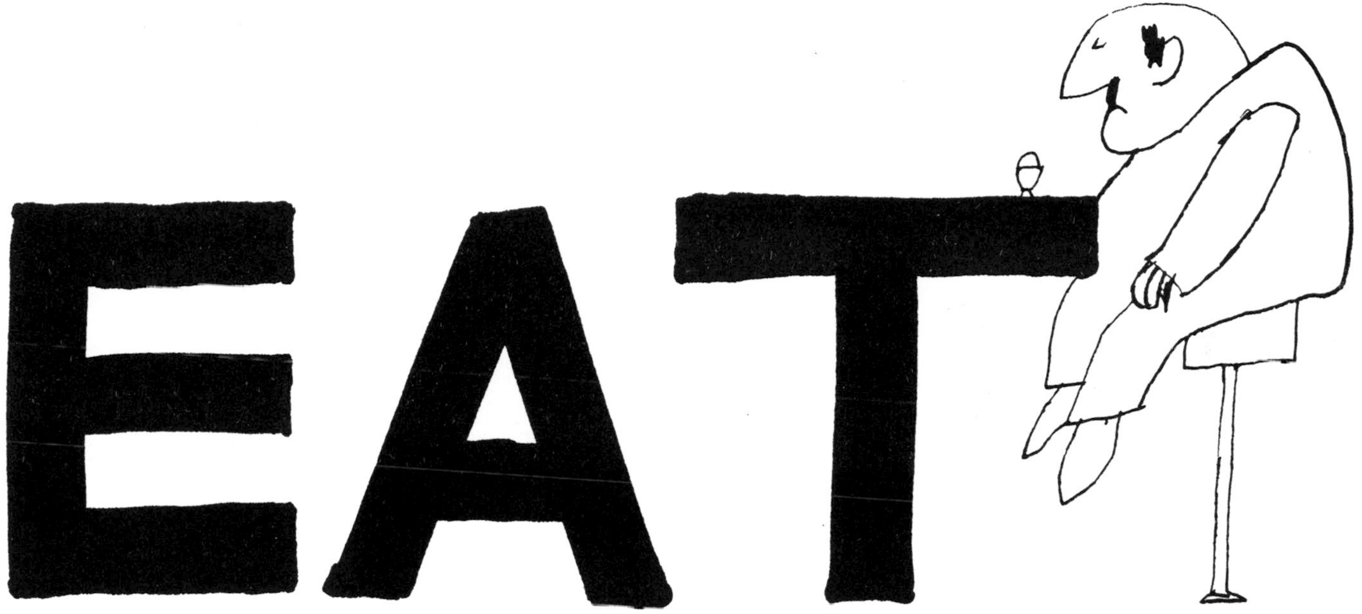
EAT

RESTAURANT DE LA PLA

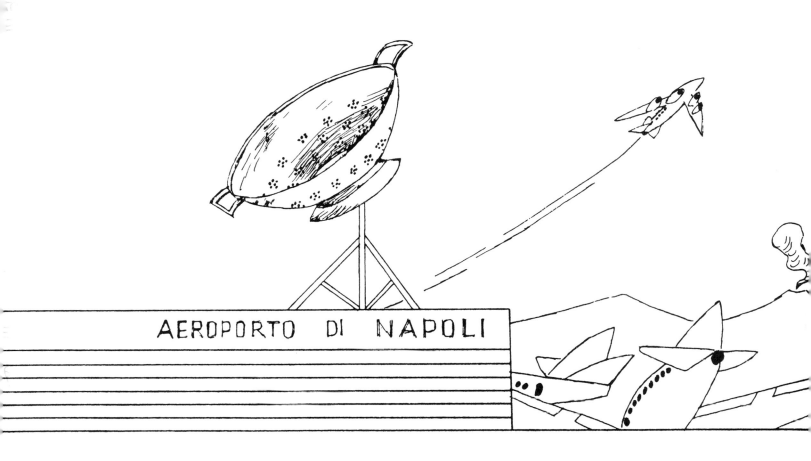

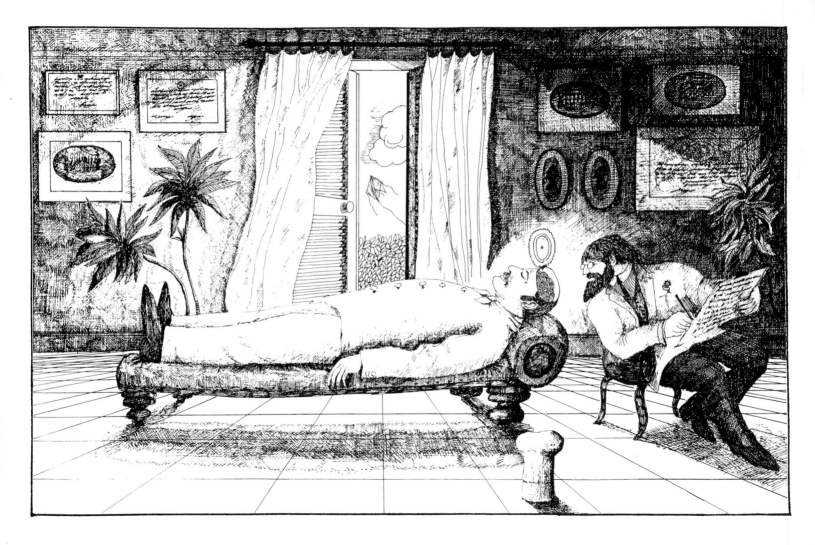

FISHMONGER
LAUREATE

apicella '90

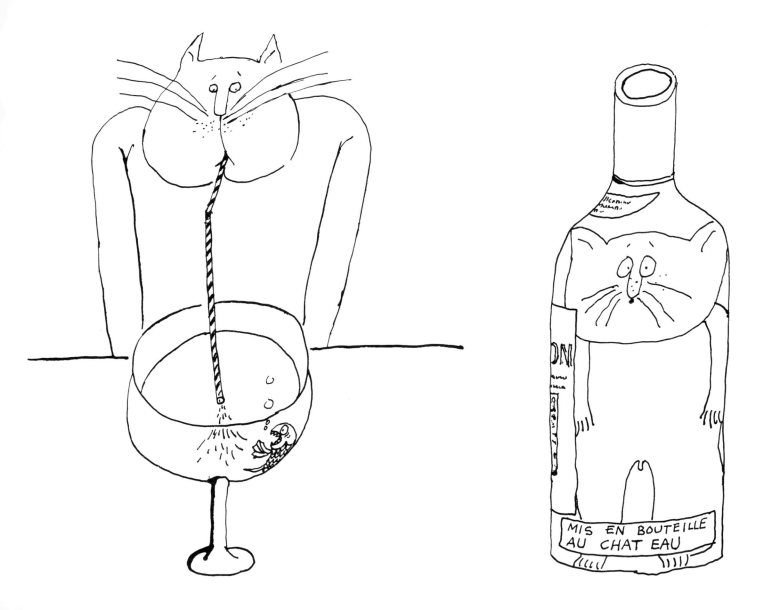

MIS EN BOUTEILLE
AU CHAT EAU

A la Recherche du Plat Perdu

AN LOREN

APICELLA

ENZO APICELLA was born in Naples and worked as a journalist, furniture designer and mural painter before designing Italy's first opera magazine, *Il Melodramma*. He arrived in England in 1954 and since then has designed advertising posters and sets for television, produced cartoon films, contributed illustrations to numerous magazines and drawn cartoons for *Observer*, *Guardian*, *Punch*, *Economist*, *Private Eye* and *Harpers & Queen* amongst others. Described by Bevis Hillier in *Vogue* as 'one of the creators of the Swinging Sixties in London', his work as an interior designer for more than 65 restaurants, notably for the Pizza Express chain, established a style which has been widely imitated. Co-founder of the Arethusa Club and Meridiana Restaurant, he is currently co-owner of the Condotti Restaurant in London's Mayfair. *Mouthfool* celebrates Apicella's first 30 years in the food business.

AU
CHEF INCONNU